QUIETING
Your Heart

GRATITUDE JOURNAL

DARLENE &
MADISON SCHACHT

QUIETING Your Heart

GRATITUDE JOURNAL

DARLENE & MADISON SCHACHT

TIME-WARP WIFE MINISTRIES

www.timewarpwife.com

Quieting Your Heart: Gratitude Journal

Time-Warp Wife
Suite 5-1377 Border Street
Winnipeg, Manitoba
R3H ON1

ISBN 978-0-9950567-6-3

All scripture taken from the KJV Bible

Images from Bigstock.com

Find Darlene Schacht on the web here:
Blog: TimeWarpWife.com
Facebook: timewarpwife
Twitter: timewarpwife
Pinterest: timewarpwife

Today's Prayer

Prayer Requests
& Praise Reports

This is the day which the Lord hath made; we will rejoice and be glad in it.

Psalm 118:24, KJV

I'M THANKFUL FOR...

1

2

3

4

3 WAYS I CAN
EXPRESS MY
Gratitude

ONE OF MY FAVORITE MEMORIES...

Today I'm Reading:

_____
_____
_____

This is What I Learned:

_____
_____
_____
_____
_____
_____
_____
_____

_____
_____
_____
_____
_____
_____
_____
_____
_____
_____
_____
_____
_____
_____
_____

Something Wonderful
That Happened Today

_____
_____
_____
_____

Today's Prayer

Prayer Requests & Praise Reports

I'M THANKFUL FOR...

1.

2.

3.

4.

3 WAYS I CAN EXPRESS MY Gratitude

➡️

➡️

➡️

ONE OF MY FAVORITE MEMORIES...

_____
_____
_____
_____
_____
_____
_____
_____
_____
_____

Today I'm **Reading:**

This is What I Learned:

Something Wonderful
That Happened Today

Today's Prayer

Prayer Requests & Praise Reports

The Lord is my strength and song,

and he is become my salvation: he is my God, and I will prepare him an habitation; my father's God, and I will exalt him.

Exodus 15:2 , KJV

I'M THANKFUL FOR...

♥ 1

♥ 2

♥ 3

♥ 4

3 WAYS I CAN
EXPRESS MY
Gratitude

⇒

⇒

⇒

ONE OF MY FAVORITE MEMORIES...

_____
_____
_____
_____
_____
_____
_____
_____
_____

Today I'm **Reading**:

This is What I Learned:

Something Wonderful That Happened Today

Today's Prayer

Prayer Requests & Praise Reports

BUT THANKS BE
TO GOD, WHICH GIVETH
US THE VICTORY
THROUGH OUR LORD
JESUS CHRIST.

1 Corinthians 15:57, KJV

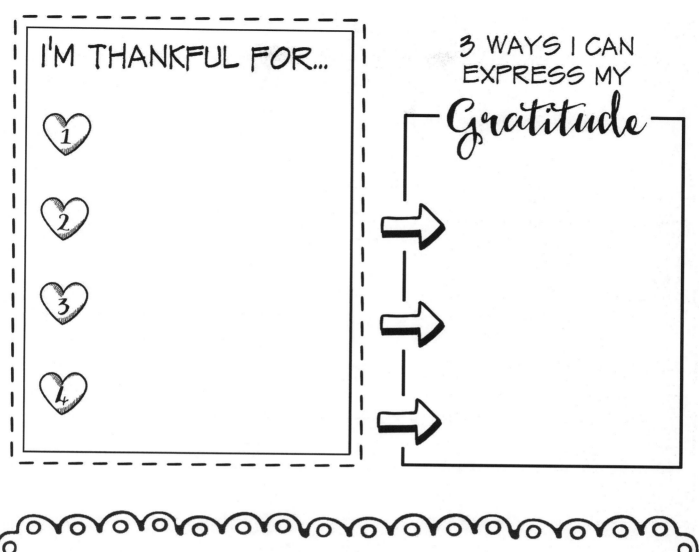

I'M THANKFUL FOR...

1

2

3

4

3 WAYS I CAN
EXPRESS MY
Gratitude

ONE OF MY FAVORITE MEMORIES...

Today I'm **Reading:**

This is What I Learned:

Something Wonderful That Happened Today

Today's Prayer

Prayer Requests
& Praise Reports

Let every thing
that hath breath
praise the Lord.
Praise ye the Lord.
Psalm 150:6, KJV

I'M THANKFUL FOR...

1

2

3

4

3 WAYS I CAN EXPRESS MY Gratitude

ONE OF MY FAVORITE MEMORIES...

_____

_____

_____

_____

_____

_____

_____

_____

_____

Today I'm **Reading**:

This is What I Learned:

Something Wonderful That Happened Today

Today's Prayer

Prayer Requests & Praise Reports

Enter into his gates with thanksgiving, and into his courts with praise: be thankful unto him, and bless His name.

Psalm 100:4, KJV

I'M THANKFUL FOR...

1

2

3

4

3 WAYS I CAN EXPRESS MY

Gratitude

ONE OF MY FAVORITE MEMORIES...

Today I'm Reading:

This is What I Learned:

Something Wonderful That Happened Today

Today's Prayer

Prayer Requests & Praise Reports

It is a good thing
to give thanks unto
the Lord, and to
sing praises
unto thy name,
O Most High.

Psalm 92:1, KJV

I'M THANKFUL FOR...

1

2

3

4

3 WAYS I CAN EXPRESS MY *Gratitude*

ONE OF MY FAVORITE MEMORIES...

Today I'm **Reading**:

This is What I Learned:

Something Wonderful That Happened Today

Today's Prayer

Prayer Requests
& Praise Reports

And when he had given thanks, he brake it, and said, Take, eat: this is my body, which is broken for you: this do in remembrance of me.

1 Corinthians 11:24, KJV

I'M THANKFUL FOR...

1

2

3

4

3 WAYS I CAN EXPRESS MY *Gratitude*

ONE OF MY FAVORITE MEMORIES...

Today I'm **Reading:**

This is What I Learned:

Something Wonderful
That Happened Today

Today's Prayer

Prayer Requests & Praise Reports

Give thanks unto the Lord, call upon his name, make known his deeds among the people

1 Chronicles 16:8, KJV

I'M THANKFUL FOR...

♡ 1
♡ 2
♡ 3
♡ 4

3 WAYS I CAN EXPRESS MY *Gratitude*

⇒
⇒
⇒

ONE OF MY FAVORITE MEMORIES...

Today I'm Reading:

_____
_____
_____

This is What I Learned:

_____
_____
_____
_____
_____
_____
_____

_____
_____
_____
_____
_____
_____
_____
_____
_____
_____
_____
_____
_____

Something Wonderful That Happened Today

_____
_____
_____
_____
_____

Today's Prayer

_____
_____
_____
_____
_____
_____

Prayer Requests
& Praise Reports

_____
_____
_____
_____
_____
_____
_____
_____
_____
_____

I WILL BLESS THE LORD AT ALL TIMES: HIS PRAISE SHALL CONTINUALLY BE IN MY MOUTH. PSALM 34:1

I'M THANKFUL FOR...

1

2

3

4

3 WAYS I CAN EXPRESS MY *Gratitude*

ONE OF MY FAVORITE MEMORIES...

Today I'm Reading:

This is What I Learned:

Something Wonderful That Happened Today

Today's Prayer

_____

_____

_____

_____

_____

_____

_____

Prayer Requests & Praise Reports

_____

_____

_____

_____

_____

_____

_____

_____

_____

_____

_____

_____

_____

_____

In every thing
give thanks: for
this is the will of God in
Christ Jesus concerning you.
1 Thessalonians 5:18, KJV

I'M THANKFUL FOR...

1

2

3

4

3 WAYS I CAN EXPRESS MY
Gratitude

ONE OF MY FAVORITE MEMORIES...

Today I'm
Reading:

_____
_____
_____
_____
_____

This is What I Learned:

_____
_____
_____
_____
_____
_____
_____
_____
_____
_____
_____
_____
_____
_____
_____
_____
_____
_____
_____
_____
_____
_____
_____

Something Wonderful
That Happened Today

_____
_____
_____
_____

Today's Prayer

_____
_____
_____
_____
_____
_____
_____

Prayer Requests
& Praise Reports

_____
_____
_____
_____
_____
_____
_____
_____
_____
_____
_____
_____
_____
_____

I will praise thee, O Lord, with my whole heart; I will shew forth all thy marvelous works. I will be glad and rejoice in thee: I will sing praise to thy name, O thou most High.

Psalm 9:1-2, KJV

I'M THANKFUL FOR...

♥ 1

♥ 2

♥ 3

♥ 4

3 WAYS I CAN EXPRESS MY Gratitude

➡

➡

➡

ONE OF MY FAVORITE MEMORIES...

Today I'm Reading:

This is What I Learned:

Something Wonderful That Happened Today

Today's Prayer

Prayer Requests
& Praise Reports

Giving thanks always for all things unto God and the Father in the name of our Lord Jesus Christ.

Ephesians 5:20, KJV

I'M THANKFUL FOR...

1

2

3

4

3 WAYS I CAN EXPRESS MY
Gratitude

ONE OF MY FAVORITE MEMORIES...

Today I'm Reading:

This is What I Learned:

Something Wonderful That Happened Today

Today's Prayer

_____
_____
_____
_____
_____
_____
_____
_____

Prayer Requests & Praise Reports

_____
_____
_____
_____
_____
_____
_____
_____
_____
_____
_____
_____
_____
_____

And whatsoever ye do in word or deed, do all in the name of **The Lord Jesus,** giving thanks to God and the Father by him.

Colossians 3:17, KJV

I'M THANKFUL FOR...

♡ 1

♡ 2

♡ 3

♡ 4

3 WAYS I CAN
EXPRESS MY
Gratitude

➡

➡

➡

ONE OF MY FAVORITE MEMORIES...

Today I'm
Reading:

_____
_____
_____

This is What I Learned:

_____
_____
_____
_____
_____
_____
_____

_____
_____
_____
_____
_____
_____

Something Wonderful
That Happened Today

_____
_____
_____
_____
_____

_____
_____

Today's Prayer

Prayer Requests & Praise Reports

Let the word of Christ dwell in you richly in all wisdom; teaching and admonishing one another in psalms and hymns and spiritual songs, singing with grace in your hearts to the Lord

Colossians 3:16, KJV

I'M THANKFUL FOR...

1

2

3

4

3 WAYS I CAN EXPRESS MY *Gratitude*

ONE OF MY FAVORITE MEMORIES...

Today I'm
Reading:

_____
_____
_____
_____

This is What I Learned:

_____
_____
_____
_____
_____
_____
_____

_____
_____
_____
_____
_____
_____
_____

Something Wonderful
That Happened Today

_____
_____
_____
_____
_____

Today's Prayer

_____

_____

_____

_____

_____

_____

_____

_____

Prayer Requests & Praise Reports

_____

_____

_____

_____

_____

_____

_____

_____

_____

_____

_____

_____

To the end that my glory may sing
praise to thee, and not be silent.
O Lord my God, I will
give thanks unto thee for ever.

Psalm 30:12, KJV

I'M THANKFUL FOR...

1

2

3

4

3 WAYS I CAN EXPRESS MY *Gratitude*

ONE OF MY FAVORITE MEMORIES...

Today I'm Reading:

This is What I Learned:

Something Wonderful That Happened Today

Today's Prayer

Prayer Requests & Praise Reports

Sing unto the Lord, O ye saints of his, and give thanks at the remembrance *of his holiness.*

Psalm 30:4, KJV

I'M THANKFUL FOR...

1

2

3

4

3 WAYS I CAN
EXPRESS MY
Gratitude

ONE OF MY FAVORITE MEMORIES...

Today I'm
Reading:

_____
_____
_____
_____

This is What I Learned:

_____
_____
_____
_____
_____
_____
_____
_____
_____
_____
_____
_____
_____
_____
_____
_____
_____
_____
_____
_____

Something Wonderful
That Happened Today

_____
_____
_____
_____
_____

Today's Prayer

_____

_____

_____

_____

_____

_____

_____

_____

Prayer Requests
& Praise Reports

_____

_____

_____

_____

_____

_____

_____

_____

_____

_____

_____

_____

Will call on the Lord, who is worthy to be praised: so shall I be saved *from mine enemies*.

2 Samuel 22:4, KJV

I'M THANKFUL FOR...

1.

2.

3.

4.

3 WAYS I CAN EXPRESS MY *Gratitude*

→

→

→

ONE OF MY FAVORITE MEMORIES...

Today I'm **Reading**:

This is What I Learned:

Something Wonderful
That Happened Today

Today's Prayer

_____
_____
_____
_____
_____
_____
_____
_____
_____

Prayer Requests & Praise Reports

_____
_____
_____
_____
_____
_____
_____
_____
_____
_____
_____
_____
_____

I will praise
the Lord
according to his
righteousness:
and will sing praise
to the name of the
Lord most high.

Psalm 7:17, KJV

I'M THANKFUL FOR...

♥ 1

♥ 2

♥ 3

♥ 4

3 WAYS I CAN EXPRESS MY
Gratitude

➡

➡

➡

ONE OF MY FAVORITE MEMORIES...

Today I'm Reading:

_____
_____
_____
_____

This is What I Learned:

_____
_____
_____
_____
_____
_____
_____
_____

_____
_____
_____
_____
_____
_____

Something Wonderful That Happened Today

_____
_____
_____
_____
_____
_____

Today's Prayer

Prayer Requests & Praise Reports

I'M THANKFUL FOR...

♥ 1

♥ 2

♥ 3

♥ 4

3 WAYS I CAN
EXPRESS MY
Gratitude

⇒

⇒

⇒

ONE OF MY FAVORITE MEMORIES...

Today I'm **Reading:**

_____
_____
_____
_____

This is What I Learned:

_____
_____
_____
_____
_____
_____
_____
_____

_____
_____
_____
_____
_____
_____

Something Wonderful
That Happened Today

_____
_____
_____
_____

_____
_____
_____
_____

Today's Prayer

Prayer Requests & Praise Reports

But I will sing of thy power;
yea, I will sing aloud of thy
mercy in the morning:
for thou hast been my
defence and refuge
in the day of my trouble.

Psalm 59:16, KJV

I'M THANKFUL FOR...

1
2
3
4

3 WAYS I CAN EXPRESS MY Gratitude

ONE OF MY FAVORITE MEMORIES...

Today I'm **Reading:**

This is What I Learned:

Something Wonderful
That Happened Today

Today's Prayer

Prayer Requests & Praise Reports

Be careful for nothing;
but in every thing by
prayer and supplication
with thanksgiving let your
requests be made known
unto God.
Philippians 4:6, KJV

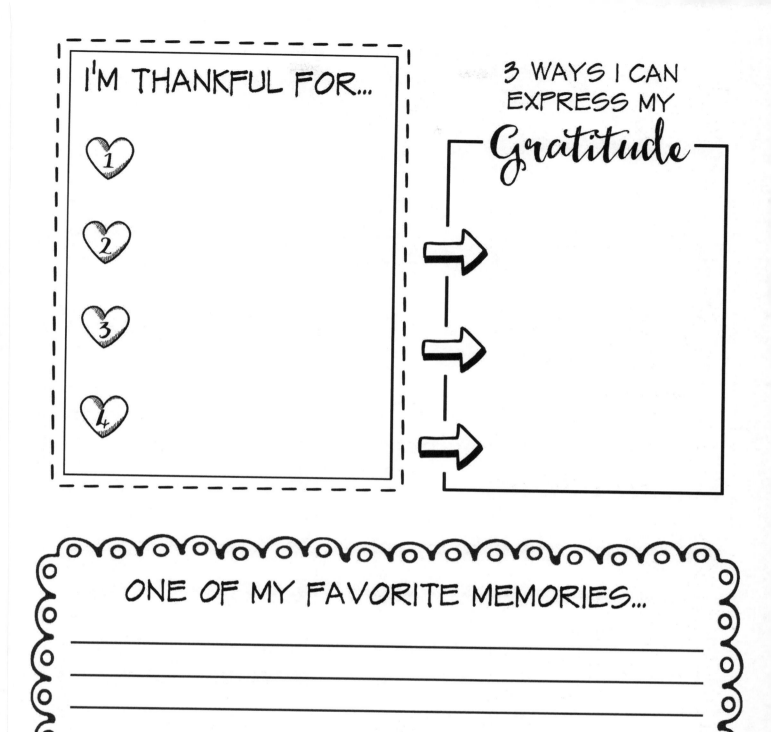

I'M THANKFUL FOR...

1

2

3

4

3 WAYS I CAN EXPRESS MY Gratitude

ONE OF MY FAVORITE MEMORIES...

Today I'm Reading:

This is What I Learned:

Something Wonderful That Happened Today

Today's Prayer

_____

_____

_____

_____

_____

_____

_____

_____

_____

Prayer Requests & Praise Reports

_____

_____

_____

_____

_____

_____

_____

_____

_____

_____

_____

_____

_____

_____

Bless the Lord,
O my soul, and
forget not
all his benefits
Psalm 103:2, KJV

I'M THANKFUL FOR...

1

2

3

4

3 WAYS I CAN EXPRESS MY *Gratitude*

ONE OF MY FAVORITE MEMORIES...

Today I'm
Reading:

_____
_____
_____
_____

This is What I Learned:

_____
_____
_____
_____
_____
_____
_____
_____
_____
_____
_____
_____
_____
_____
_____
_____
_____
_____

Something Wonderful
That Happened Today

_____
_____
_____
_____
_____

Today's Prayer

Prayer Requests
& Praise Reports

And let the peace of God rule in your hearts, to the which also ye are called in one body; and be ye thankful.
Colossians 3:15, KJV

I'M THANKFUL FOR...

1

2

3

4

3 WAYS I CAN EXPRESS MY *Gratitude*

ONE OF MY FAVORITE MEMORIES...

Today I'm Reading:

This is What I Learned:

Something Wonderful That Happened Today

Today's Prayer

_____

_____

_____

_____

_____

_____

_____

_____

_____

Prayer Requests
& Praise Reports

_____

_____

_____

_____

_____

_____

_____

_____

_____

_____

EVERY GOOD GIFT AND EVERY PERFECT GIFT IS *from above,* AND COMETH DOWN FROM THE FATHER OF *lights,* WITH WHOM IS NO VARIABLENESS, NEITHER SHADOW OF TURNING.

JAMES 1:17, KJV

I'M THANKFUL FOR...

1

2

3

4

3 WAYS I CAN EXPRESS MY
Gratitude

ONE OF MY FAVORITE MEMORIES...

Today I'm **Reading:**

_____
_____
_____

This is What I Learned:

_____
_____
_____
_____
_____
_____
_____
_____
_____
_____
_____
_____
_____
_____
_____
_____
_____
_____
_____
_____
_____
_____
_____
_____

Something Wonderful
That Happened Today

_____
_____
_____

Today's Prayer

_____

_____

_____

_____

_____

_____

_____

_____

Prayer Requests & Praise Reports

_____

_____

_____

_____

_____

_____

_____

_____

_____

_____

_____

And they, continuing daily with one accord in the temple, and breaking bread from house to house, did eat their meat with *gladness and singleness of heart*

Acts 2:46, KJV

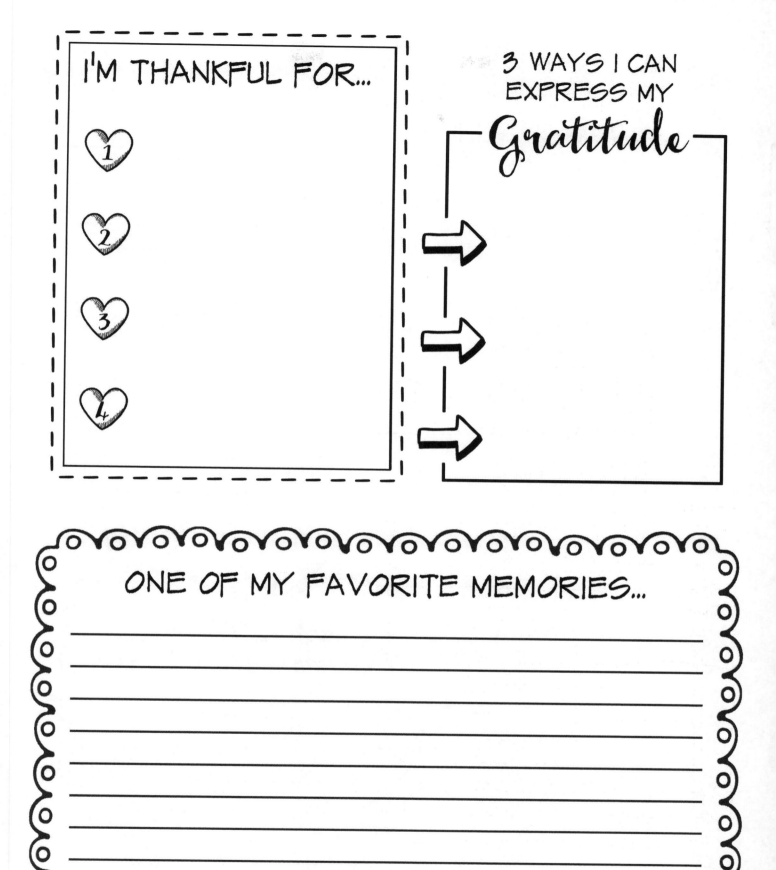

I'M THANKFUL FOR...

1

2

3

4

3 WAYS I CAN EXPRESS MY *Gratitude*

ONE OF MY FAVORITE MEMORIES...

Today I'm
Reading:

_____

_____

_____

This is What I Learned:

_____

_____

_____

_____

_____

_____

_____

_____

_____

_____

_____

_____

_____

_____

_____

_____

_____

_____

Something Wonderful
That Happened Today

_____

_____

_____

_____

_____

Today's Prayer

Prayer Requests & Praise Reports

It is of the Lord's mercies
that we are not consumed,
because his compassions fail not.
They are new every morning:
great is thy faithfulness.

Lamentations 3:23, KJV

I'M THANKFUL FOR...

1

2

3

4

3 WAYS I CAN EXPRESS MY Gratitude

ONE OF MY FAVORITE MEMORIES...

Today I'm **Reading:**

_____
_____
_____
_____

This is What I Learned:

_____
_____
_____
_____
_____
_____

_____
_____
_____
_____
_____
_____
_____
_____
_____
_____
_____
_____
_____

Something Wonderful
That Happened Today

_____
_____
_____
_____
_____

Today's Prayer

Prayer Requests
& Praise Reports

O give thanks unto the Lord, for he is good: for his mercy endureth for ever.

Psalm 107:1, KJV

I'M THANKFUL FOR...

1

2

3

4

3 WAYS I CAN EXPRESS MY
Gratitude

ONE OF MY FAVORITE MEMORIES...

Today I'm
Reading:

_____
_____
_____
_____

This is What I Learned:

_____
_____
_____
_____
_____
_____
_____
_____
_____
_____
_____
_____
_____
_____
_____
_____
_____
_____
_____

Something Wonderful
That Happened Today

_____
_____
_____
_____
_____

Today's Prayer

Prayer Requests
& Praise Reports

Thou art worthy,
O Lord, to receive
glory and honour
and power: for
thou hast
created all
things, and for
thy pleasure they
are and were
created.

Revelation 4:11, KJV

I'M THANKFUL FOR...

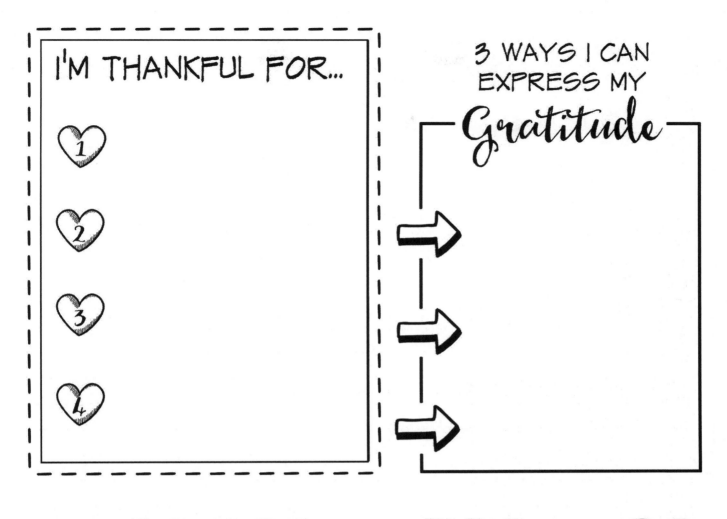

♡ 1

♡ 2

♡ 3

♡ 4

3 WAYS I CAN
EXPRESS MY
Gratitude

⇒

⇒

⇒

ONE OF MY FAVORITE MEMORIES...

Today I'm Reading:

This is What I Learned:

Something Wonderful That Happened Today

Today's Prayer

Prayer Requests
& Praise Reports

Continue in prayer, and watch in
the same with thanksgiving.
Colossians 4:2, KJV

About the Author:

Darlene Schacht, is known by her readers as The Time-Warp Wife. She's is an Evangelical Christian whose number one priority is to serve Jesus Christ in every area of her life. She and her husband Michael live in Manitoba Canada. Married 28 years, they have four children (three still at home) and a pug.

Their lives are basically surrounded with three things: faith, music and everything books.

She's an award winning and New York Times best-selling author. Darlene is also the author of the #1 Amazon best-seller, Quieting Your Heart: 6 Month Bible Study Journal.

Find Darlene on the web here:

Blog: TimeWarpWife.com Facebook: timewarpwife

Twitter: timewarpwife Pinterest: timewarpwife

If you enjoyed this book, please leave a review at Amazon. Thank you!

Made in the USA
Middletown, DE
06 July 2017